Brownies
Adventure
on

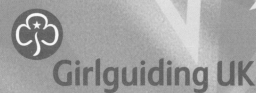

Girlguiding UK

Contents

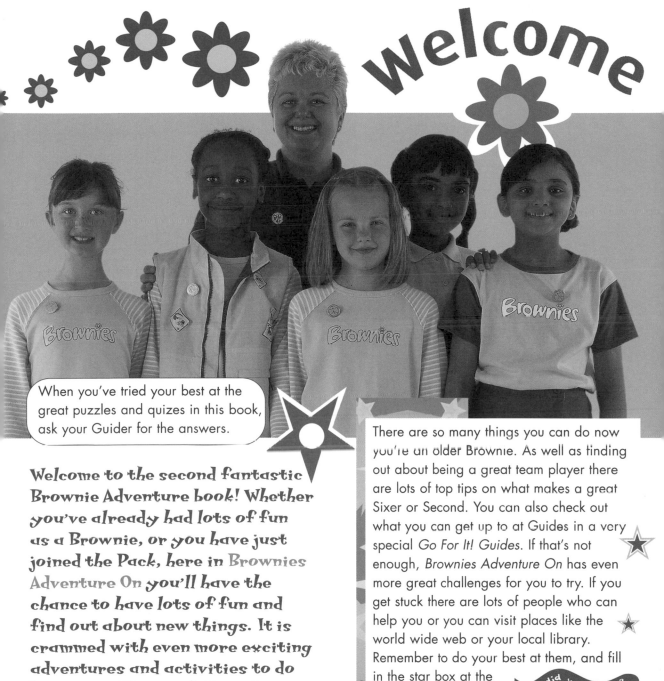

Welcome

When you've tried your best at the great puzzles and quizzes in this book, ask your Guider for the answers.

Welcome to the second fantastic Brownie Adventure book! Whether you've already had lots of fun as a Brownie, or you have just joined the Pack, here in Brownies Adventure On you'll have the chance to have lots of fun and find out about new things. It is crammed with even more exciting adventures and activities to do by yourself or with friends. There's even space for you to make a note of how it went.

There are so many things you can do now you're an older Brownie. As well as finding out about being a great team player there are lots of top tips on what makes a great Sixer or Second. You can also check out what you can get up to at Guides in a very special *Go For It! Guides*. If that's not enough, *Brownies Adventure On* has even more great challenges for you to try. If you get stuck there are lots of people who can help you or you can visit places like the world wide web or your local library. Remember to do your best at them, and fill in the star box at the end to show how you rated it as a challenge.

How did you rate it?

My fact file

I am _____ years old.   My eye colour is _____

My name is

_____

I am _____ cm high.

My hair colour is

_____

My birthday is on

_____

This is me.

My favourite colour is

_____

Practise your signature here.

My favourite TV programme is

_____

The football team I support is

_____

The film I'll watch again and again is

_____

My shoe size is _____

✳ Me at Brownies

My Promise Celebration was on

We went on Brownie holiday or camp to

I belong to _____ Brownie Pack.

I'm part of the _____ Six.

I have these Brownie badges.

The thing I love most about being a Brownie is

The best thing I've done at Brownies so far has been

My Promise

Write your Brownie Promise here, then decorate it.

✳ My best Brownie friend

My best Brownie friend is

She's _____ years old. Her birthday is on

She's part of the _____ Six.

These are the badges she's got.

This is her signature.

5

Mind bender

Are you new to Brownies? Or do you need to refresh your mind about what being a Brownie is.

2 Write your Brownie Guide Law here.

1 Where do you have your say in your Pack's activities?
a At a Get-together.
b At a Council meeting.
c At a Pow-wow.

3 Number the lines of your Brownie Promise so they are in the right order.

☐ To serve the Queen and my country,
☐ and
☐ To help other people
☐ I promise that I will do my best:
☐ To keep the Brownie Guide Law.
☐ To love my God,

4 When do you celebrate World Thinking Day?
a 22 February
b 1 June
c 10 October

5 Whose joint birthdays are celebrated on World Thinking Day?
☐ Agnes Baden-Powell
☐ The Queen
☐ Madonna
☐ Olave Baden-Powell
☐ Robert Baden-Powell

6 What does LAH stand for?

L ☐ ☐ ☐ A H ☐ ☐ ☐

7 WAGGGS is the global guiding organisation you belong to. Can you unscramble each word to show what it stands for?

1 ODWRL ☐☐☐☐☐

2 CISNTOAAISO ☐☐☐☐☐☐☐☐☐☐☐

3 FO ☐☐   4 RIGL ☐☐☐☐

5 DEGISU ☐☐☐☐☐   6 ADN ☐☐☐

7 IGLR ☐☐☐☐   8 UTOSCS ☐☐☐☐☐☐

8 Find the Six names in the snail's shell.

- ☐ Badger
- ☐ Bwbachod
- ☐ Elf
- ☐ Fox
- ☐ Ghillie-Dhu
- ☐ Gnome
- ☐ Hedgehog
- ☐ Imp
- ☐ Kelpie
- ☐ Leprechaun
- ☐ Mole
- ☐ Pixie
- ☐ Rabbit
- ☐ Sprite
- ☐ Squirrel

A little bit stuck? Ask a Brownie with the *Brownie Adventure* book or the *Brownie Badge Book* to help you find the answers.

9 What does it mean when your Guider holds her hand in the air?
a She wants to ask a question.
b You all need to be quiet and stand still.
c It's time for Brownies to finish.

10 A challenge is something…
a I can do first go.
b That I need try my best to be good at.
c Something I'll never manage to do.

11 Find someone with a Sixer badge, then draw it here.

12 Which of these people help run your Brownie Pack?
- ☐ Brownie Guider
- ☐ Assistant Brownie Guider
- ☐ Unit Helper
- ☐ Young Leader
- ☐ Pack Leader

13 How many Brownie Buddies are there in your Pack at the moment?

15 Write here the last place your Pack went on an adventure outing.

14 Name these badges.

a
b
c
d
e

What can I do now?

Being an older Brownie means there are lots of new things you'll be trusted to take on. Here are a few ideas of the extras you may do in your Pack.

- You may be needed to organise the midnight feast at a sleepover.
- You could have a special task for a week or two.
- Your Guider may ask you to help younger Brownies during games or activities.
- Be friendly to new Brownies.
- You might be a Sixer or Second.
- Your Guider could ask you to help set up games.
- Make sure younger Brownies don't get left out.
- Help hand out the letters for parents.

- Organise – and help with – clearing up after an activity.
- Be a Brownie Buddy and look after a new Brownie.
- Have the chance to do something special, like go abroad.
- Have an extra role at Brownie camp or holiday.
- Find out more about Guides.
- Be a Second or Sixer at holiday or camp.
- Collect up the equipment at the end of an activity.

Can you think what else you'd like to do?

Badges galore

Have you had a chance to do any Brownie badges yet? Or have you been too busy with other parts of your Brownie adventure? Pick up the *Brownie Badge Book* and see if there is anything that takes your fancy. Perhaps you have a new hobby or interest.

- You may be able to do one of your favourites again by completing different clauses, such as the World issues, Friend to animals or Seasons. Or you could stretch yourself by trying an advanced badge.
- There's a challenge – give it a go!

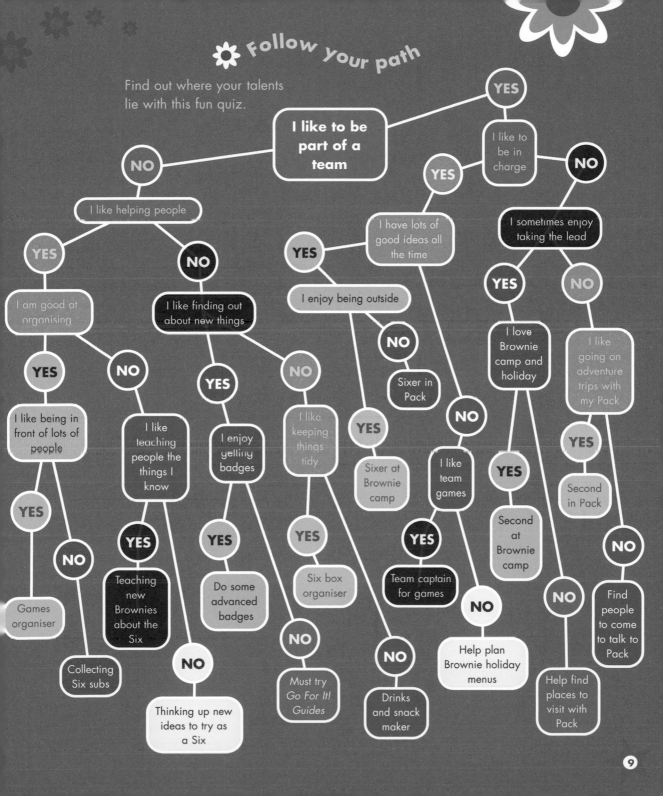

Follow your path

Find out where your talents lie with this fun quiz.

I like to be part of a team

YES

NO

I like helping people

YES — I am good at organising

NO — I like finding out about new things

I have lots of good ideas all the time

I like to be in charge

YES

NO

I sometimes enjoy taking the lead

YES

NO

YES — I like being in front of lots of people

NO

I like teaching people the things I know

YES

I like teaching people the things I know

I enjoy getting badges

I enjoy being outside

NO — Sixer in Pack

NO — I like keeping things tidy

YES — Sixer at Brownie camp

I like team games

I love Brownie camp and holiday

I like going on adventure trips with my Pack

YES

Games organiser

NO — Collecting Six subs

YES — Teaching new Brownies about the Six

NO — Thinking up new ideas to try as a Six

YES — Do some advanced badges

YES — Six box organiser

NO — Must try *Go For It! Guides*

YES — Team captain for games

NO — Drinks and snack maker

Second at Brownie camp

NO — Help plan Brownie holiday menus

YES — Second in Pack

NO — Find people to come to talk to Pack

NO — Help find places to visit with Pack

My Six's skills

Who in your Six is good at what? Put the names of Brownies next to these amazing skills. You never know who has a hidden talent!

Fabulous dancer

Great at listening

Sorts out arguments

Great artist

Wildlife explorer

Very neat handwriting

Computer whizz

Full of good ideas

Puzzle-solver

Sings like a bird

Always organised

Plays a musical instrument

Sporty

What other talents can you find?

Amazing cook

Team together

Every team needs people with different skills. Think about a netball team... it would be hopeless if everyone was a goalshooter!

> How would you get your Six to do these fun activities?

Say thanks

Make and send a Six thank you card after a visit to the Guides.

* Who would carefully measure and cut the card?
* Which budding artist would decorate the outside?
* Whose handwriting is clear and neat enough to write a thank you message – spelt correctly?
* Who knows how to address the envelope properly?
* Who would you rely on to post it on time?

Fashion it!

Put on a Six fashion show.

* Who has an eye for design to get the outfits looking stunning?
* Has anyone got a flair for advertising so others know about your show?
* Who would be best at deciding the running order?
* Has someone got a musical feel to do the backing tracks?
* Who would rather be on the catwalk, or organising backstage?

Skip on

Have a Six skipping activity.

* Has someone got a long rope? And will she remember to bring it along?
* Who will check that it's not knotted or frayed?
* Who knows different skipping games?
* Has someone got a good way of explaining clearly how to do the skipping?
* How will you decide who turns the rope, and for how long?
* Is it important that everyone has the same length of time skipping?

> **Now have a go at them**
> Did they work well? Did everyone have fun?

Top teams

Try some of these activities with your Six. They will help you work well as a team. Check at the end how much everyone enjoyed it!

Silent Sixes

Get all of your Six, including yourself, into a line without speaking.

- Youngest at the front, oldest at the back.
- January birthdays at the front to December at the back.
- Alphabetical order of names.
- Shortest to tallest.
- Shortest hair to longest hair.
- Smallest feet to biggest feet.

Try them all in reverse order. Have a go at making up your own orders.

How did it go?
- Did everyone understand what to do?
- Were you really a good team?
- How much fun did you all have?

Mime away

As a Six, mime these actions for the rest of your Pack. You can do it all together or in small groups.

- Scoring the winning goal in the football World Cup.
- Driving a car.
- Shopping in a supermarket.
- Taking part in an obstacle course race.
- Lifting a heavy weight.
- Playing a musical instrument or being in a band.
- Wrapping a parcel.
- Getting ready for a party.

How did it go?
- Did everyone get to take part?
- Could the rest of the Pack guess what you were doing?
- Were you really a good team?
- Would you do anything differently next time?
- How much fun did you all have?

Giant knot?

As a Six try to make a giant version of the shapes below using your bodies to form part of the picture. Have a go at these ideas, then make up some of your own. Try not to get tied in a knot!

✿ A car.
✿ A butterfly.
✿ The letter 'M'.
✿ A Brownie Promise badge.
✿ The Eiffel Tower.
✿ A house.
✿ A dinosaur.
✿ A paperclip.

Stretch up high to make the Eiffel Tower.

How did it go?

✿ Did everyone understand what to do?
✿ Were you really a good team?
✿ How much fun did you all have?

Be a team player

A leader is no good without a great team! A good team player supports the leader and joins in to get the best team result. Think how your Promise can help you.

Getting along

Everyone in the team needs to pull together. It's not just about what you do, but how you do it. It helps if everyone gets along, so remember to thank others for their help, and say sorry if you need to.

Do you care?

It shows if you care about what you are doing and how well you all do it. It helps get the rest of the team in the right mood, too!

Have fun!

Have as much fun as you can! It'll rub off on others so that everyone has a great time! Have a team grin or chant to show how much fun you've had. Make up one with your Six.

Friends

Are you there for your team mates when they are happy or sad, when they are having a good time or are upset?

⋆ Understand others

There are times when another Brownie is a bit down in the dumps so might not feel like joining in. Or she may not like a certain activity. Can you find out why? Have a go at getting her to join in – after all she'll never know if she likes something until she tries it! Don't forget to tell the Sixer so she can help her as well.

Fair play

When you play a game, are you fair and do you follow the rules?

Keep your Law

Thinking of others in your team before yourself really is keeping your Brownie Law. Do you give younger Brownies in your Six a chance to do the fun bits as well?

☆ Lend a hand

It may not be your 'job' but another Brownie may be grateful for your help. Just ask!

INSTRUCTIONS

Act it out

Try this with your Six team. Each Brownie picks a type of person from the list. Then you all act out one of the scenes using the personalities you've chosen.

* Miserable.
* Angry.
* Enthusiastic.
* Dramatic.
* Adventurous.
* Timid.

Scene 1 You have a tent with a set of instructions and are told to put it up.

Scene 2 You need to decide what cake you'd like to make for a friend's birthday. Then make it!

Scene 3 You are stranded on a desert island and have to work out how to get home.

* How did you get on?
* Did you work as a team?
* Would you have got the job done?
* Did anyone get left out?

Follow the leader

Q What do these people have in common?

team captain ✿ orchestra conductor ✿ parent ✿ head teacher ✿ Sixer ✿ band manager ✿ prime minister ✿ company director ✿ Guider

A They all lead teams.

What do you think makes a great leader? Have a go at this quiz to find out more.

1 Top pop band the Ugly Bugs are about to go on tour. Two members want to start in the USA and the other two think the Far East would be better. They're threatening to split. What should their manager do?

a Tell the band that they must do whatever she says. She's the boss and knows best.

b Suggest starting in the Far East, then after their last concert in the States they can have a holiday wherever they fancy.

c Get flustered, and beg the band not to split telling them that their careers will be destroyed.

2 The football team captain is taken off injured. Who is the best person to lead the team?

a Helen has spotted her chance to be in charge and orders the team around.

b Tara gets everyone together in a team huddle. She reminds them that the team is still strong, and that they can win.

c Kelly announces that they may as well give up, as the game is as good as lost.

3 Some hikers on a long walk find they are lost. Who would make the best leader?

a Jenny is sure she knows the way, and shouts at the others to follow her.

b Elizabeth stays calm, and looks at the map to work out how to get back on the right track.

c Caitlin panics and tells them they will never get home again.

4 Three teams are doing a treasure hunt. Which team do you think will win?

a Team 1 know each other really well, and have done treasure hunts before but have never won. They all want to be the leader, so spend their time arguing who would be the best person for the job.

b Team 2 have never met so Monica suggests they get to know each other and find out each other's strengths. The others like how Monica doesn't boss them and sees how everyone has a special part to play.

c Team 3 don't know each other well and pick the oldest person as their leader. They wait for her to make all the decisions and blame her when things go wrong.

Second

Being a Second is a very important job. She helps the Sixer but may also have her own special responsibilities.

Badge

This is what a Second's badge looks like. You only wear it during the time you're a Second.

Second role

Here are some of the things you might do as a Second.

- Help your Sixer set up an activity.
- Help a Brownie who is finding an activity hard.
- Help the Six get ready for a game.
- Stand in for the Sixer when she is busy doing something else.
- Help your Sixer when the Six is making a decision.
- Help the Six pull together as a team.
- Help a Brownie prepare for her first sleepover, holiday or camp.

Put your ideas here for what you'd like to do if you become a Second.

Hidden depths

How well do you know the other Brownies in your Six? Find out one fascinating fact about three of them.

Name

Fab fact

Name

Fab fact

Name

Fab fact

Knowing your Sixer

A Second is often busy helping her Sixer and other Brownies in her Six team. So just how well do you know your Sixer? This fun quiz will help you find out. You'll need to check the real answers with her!

1 My Sixer's favourite football team.

2 The name of my Sixer's teacher.

3 The first Brownie badge my Sixer got.

4 My Sixer's birthday.

5 Apart from Brownies, what's the thing she likes doing best?

6 My Sixer's pet is a

It is called

7 The last film my Sixer saw.

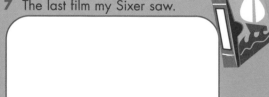

8 My Sixer's favourite band.

Sixer

Being a Sixer is a big responsibility. She is the team leader and needs to try to get on well with all the Brownies in her Six and may have to help Brownies with new activities. A Sixer still gets to take part in all the fun but will also have extra things to do.

✿ Sixer badge

You'll get to wear a badge like this all the time you are a Sixer.

Special extras

Here are some of the things you might do as a Sixer.

✿ Keep a Six record of who comes to Brownies each week.

✿ Make sure your Six is ready to start games or activities at a certain time.

✿ Help plan a special Brownie adventure with other Sixers.

✿ Help plan a Promise Celebration for a new Brownie in your Six.

✿ Tell your Guider if anyone needs extra help in your Six.

✿ Know your Six

A good Sixer is a special person. She makes sure that everyone in her Six has fun at Brownies. She needs to know them all well. What they like and dislike. What they are good at. Fill in what you know about two Brownies from your Six here.

Name _____

really likes _____

_____

but finds _____

_____ hard.

She's great at

_____

Leading the way

A good Sixer tries to help the Brownies in her Six to do their best. She'll do what is best for the whole Six, even if it isn't her own idea. She doesn't have to be good at everything herself, because she has the skill of spotting what everyone else is good at. She helps her Six use their talents to work together.

She's usually someone everyone feels happy talking to and is good at listening. She also has the knack of making the whole team get on together. She makes people feel their views matter, and is good at getting everyone involved in Six activities.

Fair enough

A Sixer should make sure that everyone gets a chance at having a say when the Six is discussing something. She must always try to be fair – even when it's something she doesn't want to do herself!

Name _____

really likes _____

_____

but finds _____

_____ hard.

She's great at

_____

How do I feel?

Draw faces in these spaces to show how you feel. Draw smiles or frowns, depending on how you feel. There is room for three weeks.

Would you say you were happy or sad this week? Talk to one of your leaders about what makes you happy or sad. Tell her what you do to make yourself cheerful if you feel a bit down.

	Monday		
Tuesday	○	○	○
Wednesday	○	○	○
Thursday	○	○	○
Friday	○	○	○
Saturday	○	○	○
Sunday	○	○	○

This is how I did my best

How did you rate it? ⭐⭐⭐⭐

⭐ You're living history

Keeping a journal or diary is a great way to record your experiences and feelings, and will also give you ideas for stories. There are many famous diaries of real and made-up people. Have you heard of Anne Frank, Adrian Mole, James Herriot or Winston Churchill? Find out about them and their diaries.

Keep a diary of the things that happen to you, your dreams and ideas, your feelings and experiences. You will find out lots about yourself.

my Diary

How did you rate it? ⭐⭐⭐⭐

This is how I did my best

Are you a bookworm?

Reading is great! You can create worlds in your imagination just by reading a book.

Books come in all shapes and sizes, and can be about anything! Do you like spooky stories, or facts on animals? Are you a poetry fan, or are you better stuck into a history novel? Fill in the books to show what you have read.

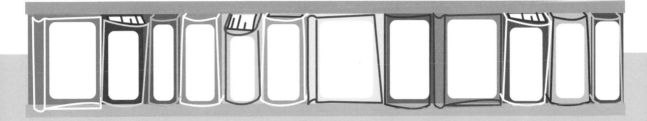

Tell a Brownie friend about your favourite book, and what made it special for you.

How did you rate it?

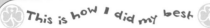

This is how I did my best

Do you love books? Read what you need to do for the Booklover badge in the *Brownie Badge Book*.

More than a book

- ❋ Are you a web-whizz?
- ❋ What about being a film buff?
- ❋ Do you love DVDs?
- ❋ Are you into computer games?
- ❋ Show a Brownie friend your favourite web site. Tell her why it's your number one.
- ❋ Which videos and DVDs would you tell your friends they must see?
- ❋ What makes a good film for you?
- ❋ What's the best computer game you've played?

Talk to a leader about your answers.

Why not visit www.girlguiding.org.uk to see how great it is!

Web safe

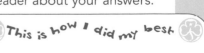

This is how I did my best

How did you rate it?

How fit are you?

Eating enough of the right foods is important to help your muscles and bones grow strong. Getting enough exercise is also essential. How active are you? Colour in these targets.

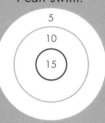

How many widths I can swim.

Target 1:
5
10
15

How many minutes I can run non-stop.

Target 2:
5
10
15

Target 3:
1
2
3

How many minutes I can skip without a break

Taking exercise isn't just about going to swimming lessons or for a jog round the park. You can exercise in lots of different ways.

This is my favourite sport

_____

This is my personal best

_____

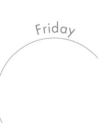

* Do you walk to school?
* Do you dance with your friends?
* Do you play football during breaktime?
* Do you do exercises in your wheelchair?

What do you get up to? Make a record of what you do every day here.

Thursday

Friday

Wednesday

Monday

Tuesday

Saturday

Sunday

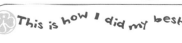
This is how I did my best

How did you rate it?

✿ Getting better

1. Set yourself a keep fit challenge. Decide what you want to do. Maybe jog every day, or join the table tennis club, or...

2. How will you go about it? Do you need to find out club times, or ask a friend to join with you?

3. Set a goal. How much do you want to improve?

4. Talk to your Guider about your plan, then get on and do it. Keep a record of how well you did.

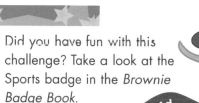

Did you have fun with this challenge? Take a look at the Sports badge in the *Brownie Badge Book*.

How did you rate it?
★★★★★

This is how I did my best

Easy to join

How easy would it be for a Brownie or leader who uses a wheelchair or who has a hearing problem to join in the fun you have at Brownies? Here are a few things you may want to think about.

- ✿ Could a wheelchair fit into the loos?
- ✿ Could someone in a wheelchair reach the worktops at your Six cooking night?
- ✿ Are there lots of steps inside, or outside, the building?
- ✿ Can a wheelchair get through all the doors?
- ✿ How would you play the games when a leader calls out what to do?
- ✿ Can things like Pow-wow or Six time be done in writing or using sign language?

What would you do about these things? Talk to one of your leaders about them.

How did you rate it?
★★★★★

This is how I did my best

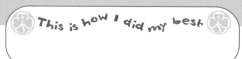

25

Teeth for life

Healthy smile

As you grow older your adult teeth push your baby (or milk) teeth out. You'll have your adult teeth for the rest of your life so it's important to look after them well.

Keeping your teeth clean and bright means looking after them. It's not just about remembering to clean them twice a day. There are other important things too, like what you eat and drink.

* Avoid sweets and sugary drinks.
* Drink water or milk instead of squash.
* Snack on fruit, vegetables or cheese rather than chocolate.
* Chewing sugar-free gum after eating can help, too.

You started with about 20 milk teeth. Over the next few years, your 32 adult teeth will appear. How many adult teeth have you got already?

Have a go at this great quiz to see how healthy your smile really is.

1 How many times a day do you brush your teeth?
  a 2
  b 1
  c 0

2 Which snack do you prefer to eat?
  a cheese
  b carrots
  c toffee

3 What do you brush your teeth with?
  a toothpaste
  b peanut butter
  c chocolate spread

4 How do you brush your teeth?
  a gentle circles
  b side to side or up and down
  c I don't bother

5 How long do you brush your teeth for?
  a 2 minutes
  b 1 minute
  c under 30 seconds

How did you rate it?

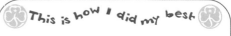

This is how I did my best

Safe as houses?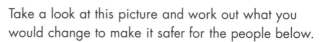

How safe is it where you live or where you meet for Brownies? What if you had an older person staying, or a new baby on the scene? What changes might you need to make so they would be safe?

Take a look at this picture and work out what you would change to make it safer for the people below.

☆ For a person with a baby or toddler.

☆ For a teenager who is visually-impaired.

☆ For an elderly person who uses a walking frame.

How did you rate it?
★★★★★

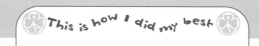
This is how I did my best

I feel good

Everyone has their own special talents. What things do you do best?

How did you rate it?

* Are you a great listener?
* Can you make people laugh?
* Are you very calm?
* Are you good at looking after people?
* Do you think of others, not just yourself?
* Are you good at sharing?

Write here some of the things that make you special and talk to a leader about them.

This is how I did my best

Dream home

Design your dream bedroom on a large sheet of paper. Or really go to town and make a 3D model in a box.

Here are some ideas to start you off.

* Where will you sleep? Do you fancy a bunk bed?
* How will you organise your clothes?
* Where will you store your games and magazines?
* Would you like a CD player or a large bookshelf?
* What will be your colour theme?

* How will you display your posters?
* Do you want a dressing table and mirror?
* What extra features do you want?

Take a look at some catalogues and magazines for more great ideas. Is there any way you could make your dream come true?

This is how I did my best

How did you rate it?

28

Not just dreams...

Have you always wanted to be a great singer? What about being a top showjumper? Do you dream about saving the planet? Fill in these thought bubbles with your dreams.

Pick one of your dreams and work out how to make it happen.

1 This is what I want to try.

2 These are the things I need to do.

3 Talk through your plan with your Guider, then carry it out.

4 Colour the line to show how you did.

I had so much fun trying my dream

I reached my dream

I did more than I dreamt of!

Why not have a go at one of your other dreams?

How did you rate it?
★ ★ ★ ★ ★

This is how I did my best

Fighting fire

If you had a fire at home, would you know how to get outside safely and quickly? With your parents, or the people you live with, make an emergency escape plan.

1 Go round your home making a map of the rooms.

2 For each room or hallway show where the exits are. These can be windows as well as doors.

3 Decide together which would be the best ways to get out of your home in an emergency.

4 Make sure everyone in your home knows the plan. Practise it regularly.

How did you rate it?
★★★★

This is how I did my best

✳ Do not stop to collect any of your things. Objects can be replaced, but people can't.

✳ Do not stop to collect any pets. Animals can often find their own way out of danger.

✳ Shout to warn other people of the danger.

Remember, if there is a fire...
☆ **Get out.**
☆ **Call the fire service out.**
☆ **Stay out.**
Do not go back into the building until the fire service has said it is safe.

Keep any keys near the door they open.

Food for all

There are all sorts of reasons why people eat, or don't eat, certain foods.

Always be careful what you give other people to eat. Allergies to food are very common and some can even kill. There are also other medical reasons that affect what people can eat.

Certain religions restrict what their followers should eat and drink. For example, cows are sacred to the Hindu religion so eating beef is forbidden. People stop eating certain foods at times like Christian Lent or Muslim Ramadan. Some people stop eating foods for moral reasons because they do not like the way it has been produced or because they worry about animal cruelty or farmers getting a fair deal. Some people choose not to eat certain foods because they don't like the taste.

What's out there for you?

See if you can find some of these foods.

- diabetic chocolate
- fairtrade coffee
- halal meat
- kosher meat
- vegetarian sausages
- nut-free cereal
- dairy-free margarine
- fat-free yoghurt
- organic bananas

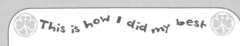

What are the prices like compared with the 'usual' version. How do the ingredients differ? Make up a recipe or meal using some of them.

This is how I did my best

Know what you eat

Take a look at the ingredients list for two makes of baked beans or jam. What's really in them? The list shows the largest ingredient first, going down to the smallest. Make a note of what you find here.

Number 1	Number 2

Which one do you think is the tastiest? Is it the healthiest one?

How did you rate it?

My Promise

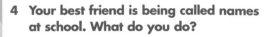

How good are you at keeping your Brownie Promise? Have a go at this quiz to find out how well you do!

1 Your little sister accidentally breaks a vase. What do you do?

a Can't wait to tell that she's to blame.
b Tell the truth and say it was an accident.
c Don't mention it at all and hope no-one will notice.

2 At school, you find a purse with money in it. What do you do?

a Check no one is looking and put it in your pocket.
b Hand it to a teacher.
c Try to find the owner yourself.

3 You watched a lot of TV last night and didn't do your homework. What do you do?

a Say you have forgotten your book and will bring it tomorrow.
b Tell the truth, you haven't done it.
c Ask a friend to help you do it quickly.

4 Your best friend is being called names at school. What do you do?

a Try to get a gang together and do the same thing to the bully.
b Tell an adult who you trust.
c Do nothing, pretending that you don't know anything about it.

5 You find a spider in the bath. What do you do?

a Wash it down the plug hole.
b Carefully put it outside.
c Decide not to have a bath.

d. Scream
e. get dad to remove it

6 You've borrowed your friend's favourite CD which you really want. What do you do?

a Tell her it's lost so you can keep it.
b Listen to it and enjoy, then return it promptly.
c Return it only when she asks.

7 You want to see a film at the cinema that your mum doesn't think is suitable. What do you do?

a Pretend to be out with friends and go to see it anyway.
b Accept what your mum says.
c Make a fuss and say you'll do what you like.

8 You're working on a Brownie badge and your childminder helps with a lot of it. What do you do?

a Tell your Guider you did it all yourself.
b Do those bits again by yourself.
c Hope your Guider doesn't notice.

9 You offer to tape a friend's favourite soap while she's on holiday, then remember you'll be away that day. What do you do?

a Go away and hope your friend will have forgotten about the programme.
b Decide to stay at home and video the programme.
c Sulk for so long that your big brother offers to video it.

10 A young Brownie is feeling left out of a Pack activity. What do you do?

a Ignore her and keep playing with your friends.
b Ask her if she's all right, and get her to join in with you.
c Wait until she looks like she is about to cry, then tell your Sixer.

11 You want a trendy new t-shirt, but can't afford it. What do you do?

a Take some money from your sister's purse, knowing you'll return it when you can.
b Ask if you can do odd jobs at home for extra pocket money.
c Persuade a friend to buy it so you can borrow it.

12 At the end of Brownie holiday you find you've taken home someone else's torch. What do you do?

a Don't tell anyone and keep it.
b Phone your Guider so she can pass the message on.
c Wait to see if something is said at Brownies.

Can you remember your Brownie Promise?

I promise that I will do my best:
To love my God,
To serve the Queen and my country,
To help other people
and
To keep the Brownie Guide Law.

Don't forget, it's a promise for every day, not just at Brownies.

33

Look after yourself

The news headlines can make the world seem scary sometimes. There are lots of ways you can keep yourself safe. The most important thing is to be aware of where you are and what's going on around you.

> Don't worry! Most kids stay safe!

> For more great tips about keeping safe, visit the Kids Zone at www.nspcc.org.uk.

Web safe

On your bike

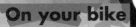

✫ Check your bicycle is working properly. Make sure you check the tyres, brakes, lights and bell. Get someone to help you if you're not sure what to do.

✫ Be sure that your helmet fits properly and that the bike is the right size for you.

✫ Don't try to carry things as you cycle.

✫ Don't wear loose clothing. Tie back long hair.

✫ Choose cyclepaths or quiet routes away from traffic.

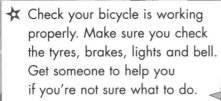

Out and about

Don't go out alone. Before you go out, always agree with your parents:
✫ where you are going.
✫ who you will be with.
✫ when you will be home.

Make sure you know your home address and telephone number off by heart.

Give your parents a phone number where you can be contacted. If possible, carry a mobile phone with you.

If you get lost in a public place, be careful who you ask for help. Look for a police officer or a shop assistant.

Never talk to strangers or take gifts from them, no matter how friendly they seem. Shout loudly and try to get away if someone you don't like tries to make you go with them or tries to make you do things you don't like.

After dark make sure what you wear is light and bright so you can be seen.

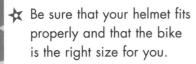

Chat with a leader and your Brownie friends about how to stay safe near where you live. Look at the stay safe challenges on page 50.

Web safe
You'll see this sign used when you need to be web safe.

☀ On foot

When you're walking remember the Green Cross Code.

Stick to main roads, and busy, well-lit areas. It's better to go a slightly longer way if it is safer than a shortcut.

If you are out and about in the countryside don't forget the Country Code. Be aware of farm dangers, and keep away from machinery and animals with their young.

Ask to your Guider for information about farm and countryside safety. What other good safety rules do you know that you should keep?

My Brownie web safe code

This special Brownie code will help you keep safe when using the world wide web. Read the rules below and use them whenever you use the world wide web.

When using the world wide web I promise:

☆ to agree rules with my parents or guardians about the best way for me to use the computer and the world wide web.
☆ not to give out my home address or phone number without permission.
☆ not to give out the name or address of my school without permission.
☆ not to agree to meet anyone who I contact on the web, unless my parents or guardians say it is all right and go with me.
☆ not to put my photograph onto a web site.
☆ to tell my parents, guardians, teacher or Guider if I find something on the web that worries or upsets me.

With thanks to the Girl Scouts of the USA for ideas contained within this warning for children.

Take a look at pages 31 and 44 of the *Brownie Adventure* book for these two codes.

Beat the bullies

Everyone is different. It could be your size, shape, colour, wearing glasses, hairstyle, accent or using a wheelchair. It's the differences that make each one of us special. At the same time, it's these differences that can give bullies something to pick on.

What makes a bully?

Bullies are often people who have problems themselves. Making themselves feel bigger than someone else makes them feel better. The things about a person they pick on can often be something they are secretly jealous or scared of.

> Don't join in with people who bully. It isn't big to make others feel small.

What is bullying

These things can all be bullying.

* Calling someone names.
* Teasing.
* Threatening someone.
* Making someone do something they don't want to.
* Making someone feel scared.
* Making fun of someone in front of others.
* Ignoring someone or leaving them out on purpose.
* Saying unkind things behind someone's back.
* Playing nasty jokes on someone.
* Hitting, kicking or hurting someone.
* Taking or damaging someone's things.

They all hurt. Having mean tricks played on you, or being called nasty names, hurts as much as being hit.

Act and find out

With your Brownie friends, act out these bully scenes together.

* One of you is being called names and made to feel small. The others watch and don't help.

* Three of you are picking on another girl. She simply walks away.

* One of you is being ignored and not allowed to join in playing a game.

* One of you is being made fun of by two girls. Another one comes to help the girl being bullied.

Talk about how you each felt. What is it like to be ignored, shouted at, picked on, or teased? How did the person being bullied feel? What about the people bullying? Talk with your Guider about how you will deal with bullying.

Take action

If you're being bullied, always tell an adult you trust, maybe a teacher, parent or Guider. They will be able to help without making it worse. Don't keep it a secret. Once you have told an adult, here are a few other things you could do.

* Write down what has happened – who bullied you and when.

* Try to stay with your friends, or spend break times with an adult you know.

* Think about and practise what you could say to the bullies.

* Try not to show the bullies that you are upset as that's what they want. Instead, try to ignore them.

* Talk with your friends – it helps to share your worries.

To find lots more helpful hints on dealing with bullies and bullying, visit the NSPCC Kids Zone at www.nspcc.org.uk.

Web safe

To talk to someone about bullying call ChildLine on 0800 1111 or the NSPCC on 0808 800 5000.

Growing up

Over the next few years, you'll be growing faster than at any time since you were a baby. Your whole body will go through some pretty major changes. You might notice the way you feel changes and also how you behave.

The main thing you should remember is that you're not alone in this! Every adult you know has gone through this journey from being a child to being a grown-up. All your Brownie friends will experience it, too. It's just another adventure!

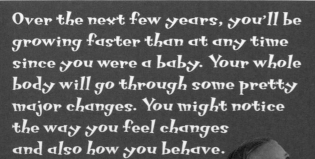

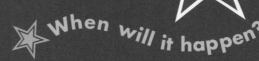

When will it happen?

You won't suddenly wake up on a certain date and find you've changed. Everyone's body develops at its own pace.

What makes it happen?

When and how your body develops is controlled by chemicals your body produces called hormones. These can affect lots of things like the mood you're in, or when and how fast you grow. Your hormones are produced in parts of your body called glands and move around your body in your blood.

Mirror, mirror

Are you happy with what you see? You should be! You're fantastic! Even though you're one of over six billion human beings on the planet, you're totally unique.

Even identical twins look different from each other in some ways. All our hopes and dreams are different as well. These things make each of us very special. Write your dreams here.

⭐ I'm special

Draw a picture of yourself on a piece of paper. Inside the drawing, write or draw things that make you special. On the outside, write or draw the things that you don't like about yourself or in other people. Can you change these things? Talk to your Guider about the words you have used.

⭐ Leg stretch

Taking care of yourself is the best way to feel good. If you're feeling a bit down, go for a bike ride or swim with friends. Exercise releases natural happy-chemicals called endorphins into your body. It also helps you look good. Your hair will be shiny and your skin will stay clear.

unfit

arty

a good friend

fun

telly addict

can be grumpy

Super six

What makes your Six tick? Write or draw three things that make each of you special. How are you all different? Which ways are you the same?

Cleansing facemask

Mix together two tablespoons of rolled oats, two tablespoons of natural yoghurt and two teaspoons of honey. Pull your hair back from your face and smear the gloopy mixture over your face. Make sure you avoid your eyes.

Chill out for a few minutes, then rinse away the mask with clean, warm water. Gently pat your face dry with a towel. Your face should feel nice and soft.

Like anything you put on your skin, if your skin begins to tingle or feel sore, remove the product straight away, and rinse your skin clean with water.

Did you have fun? Look out for the healthy challenges from pages 22 to 31.

Know the facts

Do you really know the facts about alcohol, drugs and cigarettes?

There are many kinds of drugs. Some are helpful, like medicines. Not all drugs are used for staying healthy.

Solvents

Solvents are found in lots of useful products around the house, but these chemicals can be very dangerous if you breathe them in. The fumes can make your throat swell up so it's hard to breathe.

Smoking

Smoking cigarettes, cigars and pipes causes many illnesses, like cancers, and heart and lung diseases. Tobacco contains a drug called nicotine. Nicotine is addictive, which is why smokers find it very hard to give up. Breathing someone else's smoke can be very dangerous, especially for babies and young children.

Be safe

Alcohol

Drinking alcohol can make people feel happy and relaxed. This is because alcohol makes your brain slow down so everything you do is slower as well. It can also make you feel more confident than normal. This is why drinking and driving a car is dangerous. Too much alcohol can damage your liver. Drinking too much at once can make you sick or even unconscious.

A drug is any substance that changes the way your body works.

Never take a drug without a doctor or your parents saying it is all right. Always just take the right amount. Having too much of any drug or medicine, including one from the doctor, can be dangerous.

Don't do drugs. It's okay to say 'no' and just walk away.

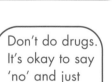

Illegal drugs

There are many different kinds of illegal drugs, such as ecstacy, cocaine, heroin or cannabis. Some drugs have lots of different names. Illegal drugs change how you feel and stop you thinking clearly. It's not just dangerous for you, but for everyone about you. The drug can damage part of you inside, or even kill you.

Loss of judgement game

Do you know what it's like not to be in control? Try this activity with a friend. You'll each need a sticky sweet in a wrapper. Stand behind your friend with your eyes closed. Your friend isn't allowed to help you, but can stop you

if she thinks you might hurt her accidentally. Unwrap the sweet and put it in your friend's mouth. Can you do it? How long did it take? Did your friend have to stop you at any point? Now swap places.

True or false?

Circle the answer you think is right.

1 Alcohol is the most widely used drug in the world.   T F

2 In the UK, about 5,000 people a year die from alcohol or in accidents caused by alcohol.   T F

3 All medicines are drugs, but not all drugs are medicines.   T F

4 All chemicals and medicines can be harmful if not used properly.   T F

5 Passive smoking is when you breathe in other people's smoke.   T F

6 Sniffing aerosols, gases and glues kills at least one person in the UK every week.   T F

7 It is possible to die after taking just one ecstacy tablet.   T F

8 Women who smoke when they are pregnant are more likely to have smaller babies.   T F

9 Cannabis can be traced in the body months after it is taken.   T F

10 Some people need medicines every day to lead normal lives.   T F

11 An addiction is anything you feel you can't do without, like computer games, coffee, cigarettes, chocolate or shopping.   T F

12 Caffeine can be found in fizzy cola drinks, some painkillers, coffee and tea.   T F

Blooming lovely

Cheer yourself up by planting bulbs to add a splash of colour to your life.

A bulb is the food source for the plant that grows from it so you don't need to do more than give it a little water. Bulbs do well in the garden, and in pots or containers.

Pick your plant

It's spring
Choose bulbs that flower in the summer like begonias, dahlias, gladioli or lilies.

It's summer
Bulbs that flower to brighten the darkening autumn days include autumn crocuses and colchicums.

It's autumn or winter
Bulbs planted now flower in the spring. Some popular ones are crocuses, daffodils, hyacinths, snowdrops and tulips.

★ Get planting

1 Plant your bulb in damp compost.

2 Leave it in a dark place. Don't let it dry out. Check it every few days.

3 As soon as the green shoots appear, put it on a sunny windowsill.

4 Bulbs take a few weeks to grow. Only water them when the soil feels dry.

Plant bulbs about two or three times the depth of the bulb, apart from hyacinths which should just stick out of the soil.

Decorate a terracotta plant pot with poster paints. Use some of the colours that your plant or flower will be. For example, for a hyacinth use pink, blue and cream paints.

How did you rate it?
★★★★

 This is how I did my best

In the frame

You need

- photos or drawings of everyone in your Six
- scissors
- card
- glue
- craft foam or card
- craft knife
- green garden canes
- sticky tape
- green card
- florists' foam or a lump of clay
- vase

Make this beautiful bunch of flowers to display photos of your Six.

1 Cut out your face in a circle. Glue it on to a piece of card. Neatly cut it out.

2 On the foam or card, draw round the face and make large petals. Cut them out and glue the picture to the flower shape.

When someone leaves your Six, they can take their flower photo with them. Remember to make another flower when a new Brownie joins.

3 Stick the flower picture to a garden cane with sticky tape. Cover the back of the flower with a circle of green card.

Why not make flowers of yourself for friends or family who don't see you very often?

4 Make a flower for everyone in your Six.

5 Put the florists' foam or clay in the bottom of the vase. Make a display of your flower photos.

How did you rate it?

★ ★ ★ ★

This is how I did my best

43

Again and again

A lot of what you throw out can be used again. So try your hand at recycling at home or on Brownie holiday or camp.

Pick one of these things.
✿ Glass.
✿ Paper.
✿ Cans.
✿ Clothes.

Find out how it can be recycled into something new. Is there a recycling centre nearby that you could visit? Contact your local council to find out. Try some of your own recycling, like making your own paper or using old plastic bottles to make a desk-tidy.

How did you rate it? ★★★★

This is how I did my best

past games

Before computer games and television, children played lots of games and made up their own adventures.

Talk to your parents, grandparents or older friends to find out about the games they used to play as children. Were there any street games, or local games they can remember? Ask an ex-Brownie like one of your leaders, a teacher or an aunt, to find out what games they played as a Brownie. Find out about the rules and any equipment you need. Ask your Guider if you can hold a games night for your Six.

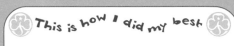

How did you rate it? ★★★★

This is how I did my best

* Get together any equipment you need.
* Make sure you know all the rules. Clearly explain them. Ask if anyone has any questions.
* Make sure the space you'll play in is safe.
* Check with your Guider and Sixer when the best time to play it will be.
* Practise before playing it for real.
* Start your own Six games book, or add it to the Pack one.

Bird life

Can you tell a swallow from a sparrow?
Do you know which birds live in your area?
Take ten minutes to listen and watch. Do
you know what you've seen or heard? Have
a go at this challenge to find out more.

Ask first

Remember to ask your
Guider before inviting
someone to your meeting.

Be safe

Ask an expert

Ask a member of the RSPB or a keen birdwatcher
who you know to talk to your Six or Pack about the
birds that can be found in your area. Find out what
they look like and where they live. Don't forget to
ask what they sound like and what they like to eat.

Do any of the birds you see only visit at certain times
of the year? Some birds, like swallows, travel to the
UK from other places, like African deserts.

Have your list of questions ready. Write them here.

1 _____

2 _____

3 _____

4 _____

5 _____

6 _____

How did you rate it?

★ ★ ★ ★

Turn the page for more Bird life challenges.

This is how I did my best

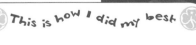

45

Big watch

At the beginning of each year, the RSPB carries out a survey called the Big Garden Birdwatch so they know what types of birds live in the UK. Find out about it and take part if it's coming up soon.

Visit www.rspb.org.uk or contact them at: RSPB, The Lodge, Sandy, Bedfordshire, SG19 2DL Phone 01767 680551

Web safe

Organise your Six to do a survey of all the birds near your meeting place, or at Brownie holiday or camp. On the right are some to look out for in the UK. How many can you spot in one week?

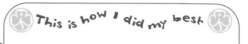

Friend to birds

Encourage birds into your garden by feeding them in the morning or early afternoon. Try different foods, like fruit, bread, cheese, finely chopped bacon rind, seeds or potato. Watch them feed. How many kinds do you recognise? It will take a couple of weeks for the birds to find your feeding station. Don't stop feeding the birds suddenly, especially during the winter, or when they are feeding their young.

If you enjoyed these challenges you might like to help a younger Brownie make the bird pudding on page 77 of her *Brownie Adventure* book. Or have a go at the Wildlife explorer or Seasons badge. Take a look at the *Brownie Badge Book*.

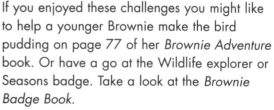

Always put food where birds can eat it without cats bothering them and where unwanted creatures can't get to it.

How did you rate it?

This is how I did my best

46

Bird	What it looks like	Where I saw it
Blackbird		
Chaffinch		
Collared dove		
Coal tit		
Greenfinch		
House sparrow		
Dunnock		
Robin		
Song thrush		
Starling		
Wren		

Animal magic

We would find it difficult to live and work if there were no other animals. Before cars, buses and vans were common, horses and ponies were used for transport.

Today, people still rely on animals in lots of ways. Can you think of three ways that animals help humans every day?

Dogs can be trained to carry out many different jobs and are really useful for people who are deaf or visually impaired. Animals can sometimes be taken into hospitals to help cheer up sick people. Many people keep pets for company.

Did you have fun with this challenge? Have a go at the Friend to animals badge. Find out all about it in the *Brownie Badge Book*.

Do you have a pet at home or at school? Write about it, or an animal you know, here.

Type of animal

Name

Age

Birthday

Colour

Favourite food

Favourite toy

Best moment together

How did you rate it?

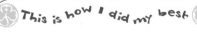
This is how I did my best

48

Happy talk

Thousands of languages are spoken round the world. Even in one country there can be many languages used.

Languages I've heard or seen

Have a go at spelling these things with your fingers.
* Your name.
* Your Six's name.
* Your best friend's name.
* The place where you live.
* Your favourite pop group.
* The best film you've seen.

Take a look at the Disability awareness badge in the *Brownie Badge Book*.

Near you

Think about where you live. Are there areas or communities where languages other than English are spoken? Does anyone you know speak another language? Next time you are out and about locally, look and listen to all the different languages around you.

Sign it!

There are many ways of communicating. Some people who have difficulty hearing use a sign language to 'speak'. Take a look at the finger-spelling alphabet – it's sometimes also called the British Manual Alphabet. It's used to spell words with your fingers.

 This is how I did my best

How did you rate it?

49

Home Zone

How well do you know the area where you live?

✦ Best and worst

Draw a picture or make a model of your favourite area of your village, town, or city. Why did you pick it? Now draw a picture or make a model of the area you would most like to change. Why? What could be done to change it?

Know your dangers

Draw a sketch of the area near your home, school or Brownie meeting place. Mark any dangers you may find. Think about these things.

* Beaches and cliffs.
* Rivers, ponds and canals.
* Roads and motorways.
* Railways.
* Litter and waste.
* Farmland and farm machinery.

Talk with your Guider about what you do to make sure you stay safe in these places.

No Swimming

Electrical Danger

DANGER Strong currents

✦ Local voyage

Take a trip on a local train, tube, tram, metro or bus. Write a poem or take along a camera to show images of your journey.

 This is how I did my best.

Don't forget to talk to your Guider about your plans, and make sure you have an adult you know with you on the journey.

 Be safe

 How did you rate it?

⭐ Water wise

Even calm-looking water can be full of hidden dangers. Swimming in a warm, indoor pool is very different from trying to swim after having fallen into cold, murky water. Find out about the Water Safety Code. Make a poster, or mime a short scene for the rest of your Six to show what it's all about.

(10m) (15m) (25m) (50m) (100m)

Learn to swim or aim to improve. Colour the distance you reach.

Web safe

Visit www.lifesavers.org.uk for more information.

This is how I did my best

Was this a great challenge? Look at the Water safety badge in the *Brownie Badge Book*.

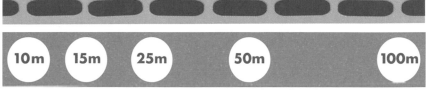

How did you rate it?
⭐ ⭐ ⭐ ⭐

Down at the farm

Find out where you local open or community farm is, and when it is open. Look in your local phone book, or see if there are any leaflets at your library or tourist information centre. With your Brownie friends or Six, organise a visit.

Think about how these things could be dangerous.
* Tractors and other big machines.
* Bales of straw or hay.
* Animals like rats and mice or cattle and sheep.
* What you touch.
* Grain silos.
* Chemicals and fuels.

Make a poster about what you find out. Don't forget to put in the good things about farms, like all the food they produce for us to eat.

Be safe

Remember to talk through your plans with your Guider.

Be safe

Before you go, talk about the dangers you could find at a working farm. Find out how farm workers keep healthy and safe.

This is how I did my best

How did you rate it?

Going away

Brownie sleepovers, holidays and camps are great ways to spend time with your Brownie friends and get to know them better. You'll also have lots of chances to try new things and have a go at exciting activities. It's all a big part of your Brownie Adventure!

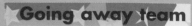

Going away team

Your Six at Brownie camp or holiday is really important. You'll be doing lots of things together, from helping cook meals to setting up activities.

You might get to be a Sixer or Second at camp or holiday, even if you're not one at your weekly meetings.

Why not...?

Take a look at these great badges in the *Brownie Badge Book* and have a go at them when you are at camp or on holiday.

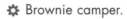

- Brownie camper.
- Brownie holiday.
- Collector.
- Cook.
- Craft.
- Seasons.
- Sports.
- Stargazer.
- Wildlife explorer.

✳ Memory board

Make a memory board to display the special things from your sleepover, camp or holiday. Each time you go away, add to it. Then display it on your bedside table.

1 Cut a 2cm strip from the long edge of one piece of felt.

You need

* ✳ 2 pieces of felt, 35cm by 25cm
* ✳ scissors
* ✳ 2 pieces of thick card, 14cm by 20cm
* ✳ glue
* ✳ sequins, ribbons, fabric paints and glitter

2 Glue the card to the felt as shown.

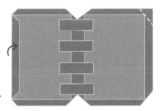

3 Snip the corners, then glue the edges in place. Use pieces of the felt strip to make hinges. Leave it to dry.

Get collecting

Try collecting some of these things to remind you of the great times you've had at your Brownie sleepovers, camps and holidays.

4 Fold the board in two. Stick the other piece of felt to one half, then fold it round the back and stick it to the other half. Trim the extra felt.

* ✿ A postcard from where you stayed.
* ✿ A bus or train ticket from your journey.
* ✿ A badge or sticker.
* ✿ A sketch map of where you stayed.
* ✿ A list of the activities you did.
* ✿ Signatures of everyone who went with you.
* ✿ A copy of any of the signs, menus or posters you made.
* ✿ A note of the funniest things that happened.
* ✿ Leaflets from places you visited.

5 Glue ribbons, sequins or glitter round the edge and use fabric paints to make a pretty border.

Every time you go away to camp or on holiday, bring back some pieces to add to your memory board. If you have room, you can fold it in half and keep it safely in your Brownie Promise Box.

pack it up

In this great wordsearch are some of the things you may need at a Brownie camp, holiday or sleepover.

```
I S E H T O L C E I N W O R B
S L E E P I N G B A G O N M A
O I O Y T R I H S T O L S O F
T P Q T I U S M I W S L E F E
H P A R E M A C I E I I T T I
A E M O R D Z W H N H P S A H
I R A J D C D X C E R A L A V
R S E U E O O Y R T P D T K G
B Q R M F K I A O H F I E N L
R R C P D T A R T F S U A K K
U W N E S T R O H S J G T O D
S E U R K D O M U N P Q O Z T
H S S L V T Q E J T M B W O X
F G R A W R S R M T Z H E H W
O W E L L I N G T O N S L M G
```

* Hat
* Book
* Coat
* Torch
* Teddy
* T-shirt
* Shorts
* Pillow
* Jumper
* Camera

* Slippers
* Tissues
* Swimsuit
* Sun cream
* Tea towel
* Hairbrush
* Toothpaste
* Wellingtons
* Sleeping bag
* Brownie clothes

Don't worry, every time you go away your Guider will give you a list of all the things you need to take.

A great Brownie holiday

We went on holiday to

We got there on

We left on

My Six was called

The theme was

The best activity we did was

The thing that made me laugh the most was

The thing that made it most special for me

⭐ Brownie camp

We camped at

We got there on

We left on

My Six was called

The theme was

The best activity we did was

The thing that made me laugh the most was

The thing that made it most special for me was

Brownie sleepover fun

My Brownie
sleepover was on

(date)

We went to

The best thing we did was

We slept at

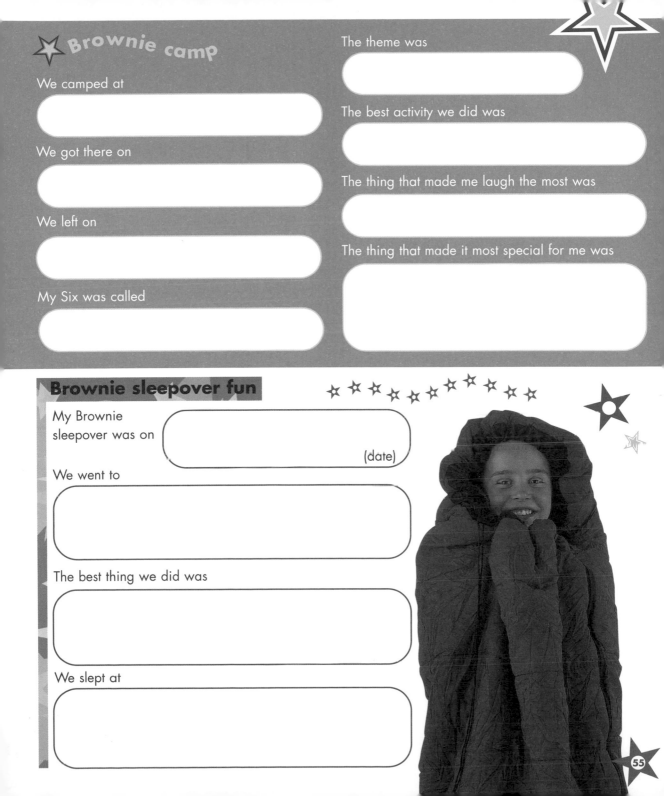

55

Make it an adventure

As you know by now, you don't have to be at your Brownie meeting to have fun on your Brownie Adventure.

Be safe

Remember, if you are planning a Brownie adventure away from your meeting make sure an adult you know, like your parent or Guider, will be with you. Take a look at pages 34–35 for top safety tips.

Be safe

Have you tried any of these great adventure ideas? Have a go at some of them with your Six or Brownie friends.

✿ Put together a stunning advert for Brownies, like a poster or a leaflet.

✿ Put on a show for the rest of your Pack, or for friends and family.

✿ Get out on your bike, or go for a nature hike.

✿ Set a trail for the Rainbows to follow.

✿ Have a health and beauty session with all-natural ingredients.

✿ Have a cook-out, or a cook-in. Don't forget to plan a scrummy menu!

✿ Try a Brownie badge to experience a new activity.

✿ Have a dance and exercise time. Try a new game or sport.

✿ Hold a party! What will you celebrate?

✿ Put on a fashion show for your Pack.

Put your own ideas here.

Now do it!

1 Take your pick

Pick an adventure idea, or make up your own idea. Write which one you'll do here.

2 Make your plan

With the others, think about everything that needs to be done. Use this space to make a note.

3 Agree

Decide who will do what. Pick a date and time for your adventure.

4 Discuss

Talk to your Guider about your plans.

5 Get on with it

Now get on with your adventure. Take lots of photos to show how much fun you had, then keep them safe in your Brownie Promise Box.

6 How did it go?

Did everyone enjoy themselves?

Did your plan work?

Would you do anything a different way next time?

Maybe you can do a special adventure like this when you are on a sleepover, holiday or camp. Ask your Guider.

Home from home!

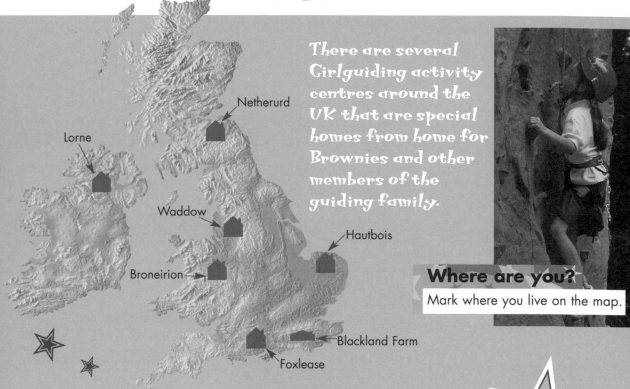

There are several Girlguiding activity centres around the UK that are special homes from home for Brownies and other members of the guiding family.

Netherurd

Lorne

Waddow

Broneirion

Hautbois

Blackland Farm

Foxlease

Where are you?

Mark where you live on the map.

⭐ Lorne

Lorne is close to Belfast in Northern Ireland near mountains, a lough and the seaside so there are lots of outdoor activities to have a go at!

Netherurd

Netherurd is in the Scottish border hills close to Edinburgh. What better place to try some Scottish activities?

⭐ Waddow

At Waddow you can camp, or stay in the main house or one of the Brownie houses. If you're feeling energetic, you could have a go at canoeing, archery or mountain biking.

Hautbois

Hautbois – you say it 'hobbis' – is near a quiet stretch of river where you can go pond dipping or canoeing. It's a great place to camp, and is close to the Norfolk coast.

Broneirion

Broneirion is in the middle of the Welsh countryside close to mountains. It's a great place for pony-trekking and walking holidays, as well as Brownie camp.

Foxlease

Foxlease has lots of rooms to stay in, including one that Baden-Powell slept in! There are Brownie camp sites and a holiday house. You might see a badger or deer.

Blackland Farm

Blackland Farm has lots of fantastic activities on offer, like team games, swimming, abseiling and an assault course. You can camp there with your Pack, or stay in one of the three Brownie houses.

Can you remember who Baden-Powell was? If not, ask one of your leaders for some clues.

Special Brownie events

There are lots of special days just for Brownies that you can go to with your Pack or a couple of Brownie friends. You might need your Guiders to go with you, too. If you want to find out more ask your Guider or visit www.girlguiding.org.uk.

Web safe

World guiding

As a Brownie you may get the chance to visit another country. Find out just how global guiding is.

1 How many members of the guiding family are there in the world?
a about 1,000
b about 100,000
c over 10,000,000

2 What are Brownies in Honduras called?
a Wasps
b Bees
c Ants

3 What does the word 'sangam' mean?
a making friends
b joining together
c having a party

4 Match the Brownie Promise badges with a country.

Pakistan   Greece   UK

5 True or false? There is guiding in over 140 countries round the world.

All over the World

One of the really exciting things about being a Brownie is belonging to the largest all-girl club in the world. Wherever you visit there will almost certainly be a Brownie nearby.

Guiding World Centres

What do India, Mexico, Switzerland and the UK have in common? Each has a guiding World Centre where members from around the world can stay. It's a great chance to learn about other people, cultures and countries, as well as guiding around the world.

Our Chalet, Switzerland

This was the first World Centre and it opened in 1932. It is high in the Swiss mountains and winter visitors can learn to ski or toboggan. Summer visitors can go for cable car rides or take mountain walks and admire the scenery.

Pax Lodge, UK

There has been a World Centre in London since 1939. Pax Lodge is the newest of the four World Centres and opened in 1991. Pax Lodge is a great place to stay while you explore London.

PAX LODGE

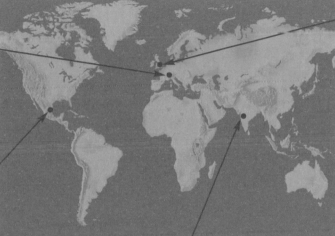

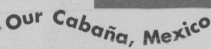
Our Cabaña, Mexico

Our Cabaña opened in 1957. Visitors can take part in regular fiestas (festivals) held in the great hall and dance to live music. Nearby is a colourful craft market.

Your own place

If you could build another World Centre – where would it be and why? Draw your design here!

Sangam, India

Sangam has peaceful, leafy gardens and a refreshing swimming pool. There's a chance to discover Indian life and culture as you explore the nearby town's bustling shops and street markets.

Find out more at www.girlguiding.org.uk or www.wagggsworld.org.

Web safe

Our planet

Life on Earth needs certain conditions. The right temperature, enough light and water and the right mix of chemicals like oxygen, nitrogen and carbon.

The Earth is made up of many layers, with liquid iron at the centre. Our atmosphere is an outer layer of gases that protects all life on Earth from the Sun's radiation.

⭐ World animals

No one knows how many species of living creatures there are on the Earth. Life is found in every part of our planet, from the highest mountains to the deepest oceans.

Make a scrapbook of creatures from different places round the world. Here are a few ideas to start you thinking.

- ⭐ Arctic polar bears.
- ⭐ Antarctic penguins.
- ⭐ Orang-utans from south-east Asia.
- ⭐ African elephants.
- ⭐ Tigers from India.
- ⭐ Alligators from the USA.
- ⭐ Otters in the UK.
- ⭐ Guinea pigs from South America.
- ⭐ Whales from the southern oceans.
- ⭐ Bright tropical fish.
- ⭐ Birds of paradise.

How did you rate it?
⭐⭐⭐⭐

This is how I did my best

Earth sun-catcher

Make this colourful sun-catcher
for your bedroom window.

1 Load the paintbrush with white paint. Flick it all over the black paper. Cut a large circle from the centre of each piece.

2 On the unpainted side of one circle, stick the white tissue paper over the circle. Stick the blue tissue over the white.

3 Cut out a small circle of white tissue paper, then cut it in half. Stick them at the top and bottom of the circle to make the North and South Poles.

4 Cut some continent shapes from green tissue paper. Stick them to the blue paper. Add some tiny green island shapes.

5 Cover the Earth with another piece of white tissue paper. Stick the other sheet of black paper on the back with the white stars facing out.

6 Tie a piece of string to either end of the cane. Stick it to the back of the black paper.

Hang the sun-catcher in your window to catch the light.

How did you rate it?

★ ★ ★ ★

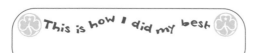

This is how I did my best

Global grub!

Where does your food come from?

Traditional taste

Many foods are associated with certain countries or parts of the world. Do you know the ones in the list below? Name where you think the foods are from, then find that place on a world map.

Draw a world map and decorate it with pictures of the foods. Taste some of the foods, if you get a chance. Which is your favourite?

This is how I did my best

How did you rate it?
★★★★★

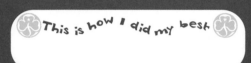

Food	Name of place	Found on map
Borscht		
Burger and fries	America	
Chapatis		
Chow mein		
Fajitas	Indian	
Haggis	Scotland	
Halva		
Lasagne	Italy	
Maple syrup	Canada	
Pavlova	France	
Sauerkraut		
Sushi	China	
Tagine	Tansania	

✿ Where it is from

Where does the food you eat really come from? Although many foods are associated with certain countries or places, more and more foods can be grown or produced anywhere.

Start with a look in your kitchen cupboard. What countries can you find in there? Take a look at the labels and see what they tell you.

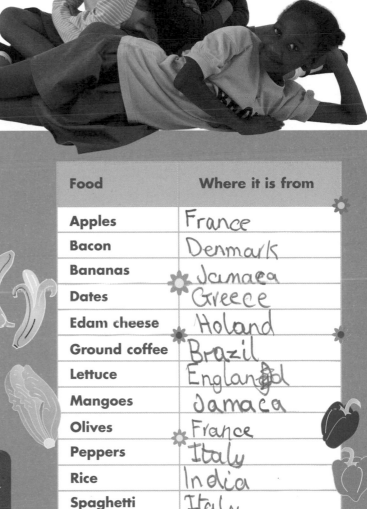

Take a visit to your local supermarket and see if you can find some of the foods listed on page 64. Where are they produced?

When you are at the supermarket, look out for the food on the right. See where they are made or grown.

Were there any surprises? Did they all come from where you thought? Talk to a leader about what you found.

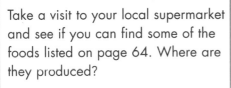

How did you rate it?

★ ★ ★ ★ ★

This is how I did my best

Food	Where it is from
Apples	France
Bacon	Denmark
Bananas	Jamaca
Dates	Greece
Edam cheese	Holand
Ground coffee	Brazil
Lettuce	England
Mangoes	Jamaca
Olives	France
Peppers	Italy
Rice	India
Spaghetti	Italy
Taco shells	Mexico

Exotic foods

On a windowsill or in a greenhouse, grow an exotic vegetable, fruit or flower from a stone or seed.

You need

- pips or stones from fruit, like a peach, melon, orange or grapefruit
- yoghurt pot with holes punched in the bottom, or small flowerpot
- potting compost
- plastic bag
- rubber band
- old saucer or drip tray

1 Fill the yoghurt pot or flowerpot with potting compost.

2 Push the pips or stone about 2cm below the surface. Water well.

3 Put the pot into the plastic bag and secure it with the band. Then stand it on a drip tray.

4 Put in a warm place. Water it once a week, or if the compost is dry.

5 After about three weeks, green shoots should appear. Remove the plastic bag and put the pot on a sunny windowsill.

Be patient. It will take years before it will be full size and have fruit. In the meantime you should have an interesting plant.

6 Water the plant when the soil feels dry.

How did you rate it?

This is how I did my best

WAGGGS

WAGGGS stands for the World Association of Girl Guides and Girl Scouts. It's the organisation that links all Brownies and Guides around the world.

Countries that make up WAGGGS are organised into five regions.
- ★ Africa.
- ★ Arab.
- ★ Asia Pacific.
- ★ Europe.
- ★ Western Hemisphere.

Web safe

Visit www.wagggsworld.org or take a look at page 90 of *Brownie Adventure* if you want to find out more.

You need
- ★ kitchen roll
- ★ mug
- ★ large mixing bowl
- ★ metal spoon
- ★ sieve
- ★ 3 tablespoons plain flour
- ★ 4 tablespoons water
- ★ plastic drinking straws
- ★ paints and brush
- ★ wool

Africa

For centuries, women in central Africa have worn beautifully decorated collar-style necklaces. You could have a go at making your own beads and necklace.

1 Tear the kitchen roll into enough small pieces to fill about four mugs. Cover with warm water. Soak for a few minutes.

2 Mix the paper into a pulp. Squeeze through the sieve. Put it back in the bowl.

3 Mix the flour and water into a gluey paste. Add it to the paper. Mix well.

4 Take a blob of the paper pulp. Press it round a straw to make a bead.

5 Make lots of beads in different shapes and sizes.

6 When they are partly dry take them off the straw and leave them on a plate to dry.

7 Paint the beads. Leave them to dry. Then thread them onto the wool.

How did you rate it?

★★★★★

 This is how I did my best

Turn the page for more from the other WAGGGS regions.

WAGGGS

Arab

Arab region includes Egypt, Kuwait, Lebanon and the United Arab Emirates. Falafel is a tasty vegetarian dish eaten there.

You need

- colander
- potato masher
- mixing bowl
- grater
- fork
- cup
- plate
- cling film
- fish slice
- frying pan

Ingredients

- 410g can of chickpeas
- 1 medium onion
- 1½ teaspoons mild curry powder
- pinch of salt
- ground black pepper
- 3 teaspoons coriander
- medium egg
- little olive oil

① Rinse the chickpeas under cold running water. Leave to drain. Mash well in the bowl. Grate the onion.

Get an adult you know to help you in the kitchen.

Be safe

② Add the onion, curry powder, salt, pepper and coriander to the bowl. Mix well.

③ Beat the egg. Add to the bowl and mix to make a paste.

④ Make eight balls. Flatten each slightly. Put them on a plate, cover with cling film then chill for an hour in the fridge.

⑤ Heat the oil. Cook four falafels at a time. When one side is golden-brown turn over to cook the other side. Try serving them warm in a pita bread with salad.

How did you rate it?

This is how I did my best

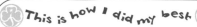

Asia Pacific

Australia, India, Japan, Malaysia, the Philippines and South Korea are just some of the countries from this region. Try making these delicious fruity chapatis.

You need

- ❀ large mixing bowl
- ❀ spoon
- ❀ frying pan
- ❀ large spoon
- ❀ fish slice

① Mix together the flour, baking powder, sugar, eggs, milk, banana and salt.

② Carefully heat some ghee or oil in a pan. Fry large spoonfuls of the mixture until golden-brown on both sides. Serve the chapatis warm with some of your favourite ice-cream.

Ingredients

- ✹ 500g wheat flour
- ✹ 1 teaspoon baking powder
- ✹ 250g sugar
- ✹ 2 eggs
- ✹ 125ml milk
- ✹ 250g mashed banana
- ✹ a pinch of salt
- ✹ some ghee or oil

How did you rate it?
★ ★ ★ ★

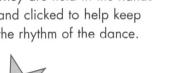

This is how I did my best

Be safe Get an adult you know to help you in the kitchen.

Europe

Castanets are used by flamenco dancers in Spain. They are held in the hands and clicked to help keep the rhythm of the dance.

① Fold the card into three and glue it together. Leave it to dry.

←—15cm—→

② Fold the strip in half. Glue the 2p pieces to the insides. Leave them to dry.

③ Decorate the castanets with felt-tipped pens, sequins and feathers, or cover them with felt.

You need

- ✹ stiff card 15cm by 15cm
- ✹ glue
- ✹ two 2p pieces
- ✹ felt-tipped pens
- ✹ sequins
- ✹ feathers
- ✹ felt for decoration

Hold the castanets between your thumb and first three fingers. Dance as you click them together.

Turn the page for another WAGGGS region activity.

How did you rate it?
★ ★ ★ ★

This is how I did my best

69

WAGGS

Western hemisphere

For the Hosay festival in Trinidad and Tobago, people dress in bright clothes and braid their hair. Have a go at this great hair-braiding activity with a friend.

You need

- ☆ brush or comb
- ☆ thick wool
- ☆ scissors
- ☆ kirby grips

1 Brush the hair well.

2 Cut a length of wool twice as long as the hair length. Fold it in half.

3 Make a strand of hair the thickness of the wool.

4 Hold the wool near the roots. Fix it with a grip.

5 Plait the two strands of the wool with the hair.

6 Bind the bottom with another piece of wool. Remove the grip.

Do as many strands as you want to using different coloured wools. Swap with your friend and have your hair done.

How did you rate it?

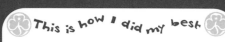
This is how I did my best

Rights

Which of these statements are important to you and your Brownie friends? Discuss what you think with your Guider. ☆

- ✳ It is important for children of my age to go to school.
- ✳ It's wrong not being allowed to watch television when you want.
- ✳ Clean drinking water is easy to get – just turn on the tap.
- ✳ If someone is ill they should get all the medical treatment they need for free.
- ✳ Playing games fairly is more important than winning.
- ✳ Parents should make all decisions for children.
- ✳ It's okay to ignore bullying.
- ✳ It's wrong for children to fight in wars.

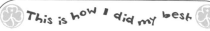
This is how I did my best

Camouflage

How many animals can you think of that have special markings or patterns on their coats?

These often help them blend in with their surroundings so they can hide from other animals.

The Arctic fox is white so it can blend in with the snow all around it.

The markings on this moth look like eyes to scare away birds that might be thinking of it as a meal. The bird thinks it is looking at a larger bird.

Zebras' stripes help them stay safe as a herd. When they all run together, the stripes make their outlines become blurry. This makes it harder for their predators to pick out one zebra and chase it.

It's not just animals that use camouflage. Soldiers dress to blend in with their background.

Hide away

Dream up two outfits for each of these places. One that will make you stand out, and one to make you blend in.

☆ Shopping centre.
☆ Park.
☆ Library.
☆ Brownie holiday.
☆ Beach.
☆ Theme park.
☆ Cinema.
☆ Moon.

Designer camouflage

Have a go at creating a 'new' animal. Design a pattern you like, and use it to make up a creature. What will you call it?

This is how I did my best

How did you rate it?

Amazing women

Q What do Agnes Baden-Powell, Princess Anne, Julie Walters, Kylie Minogue and Beatrix Potter all have in common?

A They are all amazing women. Do you want to be like any of them? What makes a wonderful woman? What do you admire in them?

Sport

Denise Lewis UK athlete
Serena and Venus Williams super tennis sisters
Tanni Grey-Thompson ▶ paralympic champion and TV presenter

✿ Acting

Halle Berry first black woman to win the Best Actress Oscar
Judi Dench Oscar-winner ▲

✿ Inventiveness

◀ **Agnes Baden-Powell** helped start guiding
Marie Curie Nobel Prize-winning scientist
Amy Johnson first female pilot to fly from Australia to London

Music

Evelyn Glennie percussionist ▶
Madonna pop superstar
Lesley Garrett opera singer

✿ Adventure

Ann Bancroft the first woman to travel over ice to the North and South Poles
Ellen McArthur sailed by herself around the world
Helen Sharman astronaut

The Queen

The Queen is Britain's Head of State. She is a great animal-lover, especially horses and dogs. As a teenager she passed mechanical courses and learned to drive. She was a Guide and a Sea Ranger. She is now a Patron of Girlguiding UK. She does hundreds of public duties every year and travels round the world meeting people.

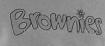

Politics

Margaret Thatcher first female British Prime Minister
Betty Boothroyd was Speaker of the House of Commons
Barbara Castle helped introduce breathalyser tests

Princess Anne

Princess Anne works very hard for many charities. She is an expert horsewoman, and was a European champion. In 1976, she represented the UK at the Olympic Games and was the BBC's Sports Personality of the Year in 1971. Princess Anne's official title is The Princess Royal.

Fashion

Mary Quant designed the miniskirt
Coco Chanel designed the little black dress
Stella McCartney refuses to use leather and fur in her designs

Business

Anita Roddick founded The ▶ Body Shop
Stella Rimmington first female head of MI5
Nicola Horlick made a fortune on the stock markets

Books

Enid Blyton wrote hundreds of great books
JK Rowling created Harry Potter ▶
Jacqueline Wilson tells life like it is

Environment and animals

Jane Goodall conservation of chimpanzees
Dian Fossey conservation of gorillas

Your amazing women

Have you got any amazing women in your life? What about your mum, or a teacher? How about your Guider? Or your nan? Your best friend, Sixer or Brownie Buddy?

What qualities do you think a super woman needs?

Which woman most inspires you? Why?

What are your strengths and skills?

73

Get ready for new things

You may be almost at the end of being a Brownie but there are still lots of things you can do.

Get to be a Guide

Are you ready for going on to Guides? Turn to page 76 to find out more.

 School

Are you about to go to a different school? Here are some great ideas to help you get ready.

Find out what they wear. Draw a picture here.

Ask your friends there for the names of the best teachers. And the ones no-one likes!

What times are the breaks?

How many lessons are there a day?

How many of your classmates are moving? Will you know anyone from Brownies there? Maybe your old Sixer or Pack Leader goes to that school. Write their names here.

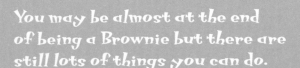

Further ahead

⭐ When you leave school is there anything you really want to do? Have you thought about what you might need to do to get there?

⭐ What will you need to do best at in school?

Can you take part in 'Take our daughters to work'? To find out more ask your Guider, or visit www.girlguiding.org.uk.

Web safe

Other new things

Which of these have you experienced?
- ○ New baby brother or sister.
- ○ New home.
- ○ New bike.
- ○ New pet.
- ○ New shoes.
- ○ New friends.
- ○ New Brownie Pack.
- ○ New bedroom.
- ○ New car.
- ○ New teeth.

⭐ Other new things you have done.

⭐ What was the best bit about new things happening?

Write here the things that you have got better at by being a Brownie.

Getting better

Have you noticed how much more you can do than some of the younger Brownies? This is because you have grown up so much in the last three years.

Sometimes it's hard to see just how much you've improved at things. Think about some of your Brownie challenges. How much better are you at them now? Maybe you had never cooked before and now you have made your first cake or done a cook-out. Were you a bit unsure about sport, and now you're a top game player?

Get the Guide facts

There's a lot of fun waiting for you in Guides! Guides are really busy people – they play games, make things, get out and about, go on outings, have holidays or camps, get badges... and still find time to have a chat and share a laugh!

Just like you?

Guides aren't as different as you think! They do lots of things that are a bit like Brownies. Here are some Guide facts to get you going.

Patrol time

A **Patrol** is like a Six. It's a great group of friends. They do everything as a team, and have a good laugh. Patrols have **Patrol Leaders** and **Seconds**, sort of like Sixers and Seconds. Here are their badges.

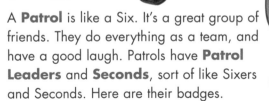

Top teams

It's up to each Patrol to make up its mind about what it wants to do – and get on with it! So all the Guides have to be good at getting along together. They're used to listening to each other and letting everyone put her ideas forward. Then they make their decision!

Top tip

A Guide 'Pack' is called a unit.

Guides go for it!

Patrols can choose what they want to do from hundreds of exciting activities in special packs called **Go For Its!** There are Go For Its! with all sorts of themes, like animals, healthy eating, parties and water.

The special *Go For It! Guides* that starts on the next page will give you an idea of what Guides is all about.

Unit meetings

Guides have a **Guider** to look after them at meetings and to help them organise activities. Apart from their Patrol time, Guides love doing things with the rest of their unit. Their Guider will sort out games and activities, like a whole meeting with a theme or a treasure hunt.

Promise and Law

Guides make their **Guide Promise** and have a **Law**. They wear a **Promise badge**, too.

The Guide Promise is really like your Brownie one.

Badges

Guides can have a go at lots of **badges**, too.

Guide clothes

Guides can choose their clothes from a range of **Guide wear**. Here are just a few of the things they can choose.

Camps and holidays

One of the best things about being a Guide is that you get to go away on **camp** or **holiday** and have **Patrol sleepovers**.

Get organised

Instead of Adventure books, Guides have this trendy personal organiser called the **G file**. It's packed with information about Guides, as well as space to write things in. There's a great calendar with stickers for those special Guide events!

Go for it! Turn the page!

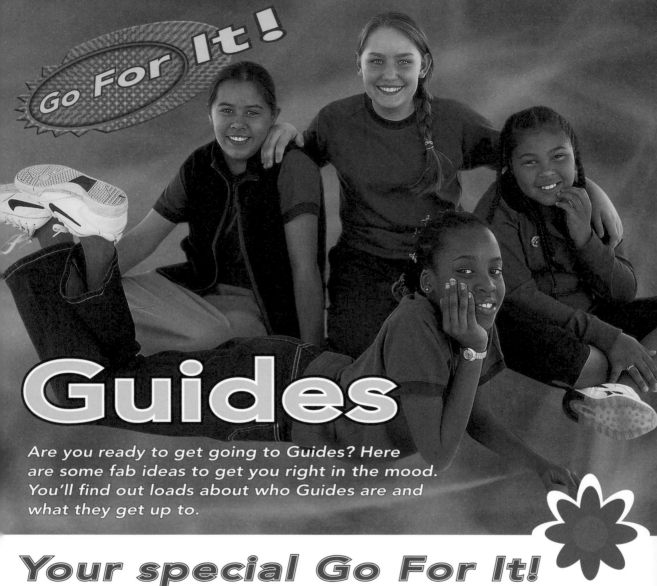

Go For It!

Guides

Are you ready to get going to Guides? Here are some fab ideas to get you right in the mood. You'll find out loads about who Guides are and what they get up to.

Your special Go For It!

Now you've read what a Go For It! is why not have a go at one? This is an extra-special Go For It! written just for you!

> Go For It! Guides will give you a taster of what Guides is like, and you'll get to find out what they are like before you join them.

Six time

You'll probably need to get your Six involved, so check with them if they fancy joining in. Or you may be able to do activities with your Brownie friends who are also thinking of going to Guides.

Certificate

If a Patrol does four activities from one Go For It! pack each Guide gets a special Go For It! mini-certificate that she can slot into the back of her *G file*.

If you choose and do four activities from this amazing Go For It! Guides you can start off your great mini-certificate collection with this fantastic card.

Going for it

Every time you start a new Go For It! activity think through these things first.

* In Guides, the whole Patrol chooses what activity to do. You might do something that's not your number one choice. You may need a mini-Pow-wow to agree what activities you're going to do.

* Check out your ideas with your Guider.

* Is there anything you need for your activity? Decide who'll bring what along.

* Do you need to ask your Guider for any special equipment or help?

There's a bit of space at the end of some activities so you can write down your ideas and any notes to jog your memory.

Have a chat with your Guider before you start so she knows what you are up to.

Be safe

Spread the word

Don't forget to show this Go For It! to someone at home so that they can find out a bit about what you might do when you go to Guides!

How did it go?

At the end of each activity, remember to tick the face that shows how much fun you had.

Go for it!

The real fun bit is doing it. So just get on and go for it!

Fact-finding mission

Well, the best way to find out what Guides get up to is to ask a Guide! Have a go at these amazing fact-finding activities.

Invite a Guide – or even a whole Patrol – to visit you at Brownies. Ask her to pick a challenge from a Go For It! pack that you can all do together. Your Pack Leader will be able to help you invite a Guide or a Patrol. Give her, or your Guider, your invitation to pass to the Guide's Guider

Send an invite

Get your creative head on and design an invitation.

Don't forget to say:

* ✿ when and where you meet.
* ✿ what time to turn up.
* ✿ what you'd like the Guide to do!

See for yourself

Can she bring along a couple of Go For It! packs so you can take a peek at them?

Top tip

Remember to check your plans with your Guider.

What's their word

What other activities has her Patrol tried from the Go For It! packs? How did they pick what to do? How did it all work out? Did they all enjoy doing the activities? What other Go For Its! can they choose from? Has she got any Go For it! certificates to show you?

Remember!

Things we need to do.

What we need to get together.

How did it go?

Twenty questions!

Make a list of 20 questions and interview a Guide. Here are a few ideas to start you off, then add some of your own.

1 What's the best thing you've done as a Guide in the last year?

2 What do you get up to with your Patrol?

3 Who decides what you're going to do?

4 What's the most exciting thing your Patrol has done?

5 What's a Patrol sleepover like?

6 Tell me about Guide camp or holiday.

7 What do you wear for Guides?

8 What's your favourite Go For It! pack?

9 Who is your Patrol Leader?

10 What's her hobby?

11

12

13

14

15

16

17

18

19 What's the next thing your Patrol is planning to do?

20 May I join in?

Remember to keep a note of the answers.

How did it go?

Top tip

If you've got a Pack Leader, ask her what it's like to be a Guide.

Get to Guides

Get yourself to a Guide meeting to see for yourself what they really get up to!

Top tip

Take a Brownie friend along with you.

Take the chance!

Ask your Pack Leader or Guider to help you sort it out. She can have a chat with the Guide Guider about when would be a good time for you to go along.

Join in

You might feel a bit strange when you first get to Guides – do they seem big and busy? Don't worry – their Guider will probably ask someone to look after you. You'll soon realise they're a really friendly bunch.

Remember to check your plans with your Guider.

Don't forget to find out where and when they meet! Fill in all the facts here.

I'm going to visit   Guide unit

They meet on

Their meetings start at   and

end at

They meet at

The Guider's name is

Her telephone number is

I already know these Guides

For my Guide visit I need to remember to take

Remember to check out how you will get there and get home. Make sure that your parents know where you will be and when Guides will end.

Be safe

Eagle eyes

How many of these things can you spot at the Guide meeting?

- ★ G file
- ★ Gilet
- ★ Go For It! packs
- ★ Patrol badge
- ★ Patrol Second badge
- ★ Promise badge
- ★ Rugby shirt
- ★ Welcome pack
- ★ World badge
- ★ The unit's Guidelines

How do they do it?

Get the full facts on what Guides do at their meetings.

How do they start?

Have they got a great way to end their meetings?

What do they do in between?

Get your Guide friends to write you a message here.

Remember!

Things I need to do.

What I need to get together.

Visit them away

If you're really lucky you may be able to spend a day with the Guides at their camp or holiday. Chat with your Pack Leader or Guider about organising this.

How did it go?

Team tactics

Being in a Guide Patrol is all about being a team – deciding together what to do, then doing it!

Dance routine

Think of your favourite group – when they do a dance routine they each have a special role. They all work together so it looks good.

With your Six make up a dance routine to your favourite song. Agree together what each person will do – and when! Will you dance in twos or threes for some parts, then all together for other bits? How will you fit your actions to the music?

When you've sorted out your routine, practise it. When it's really good do a star turn for the rest of your Pack.

Guide agreement

Did you know that Guide units make their own rules about most things? They call them Guidelines. Everyone agrees to them then signs them – the Guiders, too! They may have something about listening to each other in their Guidelines. Ask your Pack Leader to show you her unit's Guidelines.

Remember!

Things we need to do.

What we need to get together.

How did it go?

Getting to know you

Try this fab game with your Brownie friends to find out how well you know each other.

1 Each Brownie takes a sheet of paper and cuts it into six equal pieces.

2 Without letting anyone else see, each Brownie writes one of these things on a different piece:

* her birthday.
* her address.
* her favourite meal.
* the worst thing about school.
* her number one soap star.
* her dream holiday destination.

4 APRIL
MATHS 21×7 =
Jamaica

3 Put all the pieces of paper face down on a table and move them around so they are all mixed up.

4 The first player picks up one piece and tries to guess who wrote it. If she's right she can keep the paper. If she's wrong, she finds out who wrote it, then that piece of paper is thrown away.

Listen up!

Just like at Brownies, there are times at a Guide meeting when it is important for you to listen. You might need to find out what you'll be doing at camp, or when to be at the burger bar!

5 The second person then has her go.

6 Keep going until all the pieces of paper have been picked.

The winner is the person who has the most pieces. She is the one who knows everyone best!

How did it go?

Open ears

How does it feel when no one is listening to you? Are you all ears when someone is talking to you?

With your Brownie friends have a go at making up rules about listening, starting with each letter of the word 'listen'. For example, for 'I' you might decide on 'I won't talk when someone else is talking'. Fill in what you agree here.

L

I

S

T

E

N

When you have your rules try to keep them at one of your meetings! How easy was it?

How did it go?

85

The guiding game

Do you like playing games? Guides play lots of games, and sometimes organise their own games. How about you and your Brownie friends organising a game for your Pack?

1 First, make a list of the games you know, then agree the one you all enjoy playing.

> Finding it hard to make up your mind? Look at 'Six of the best' opposite.

2 Do you need any equipment? Who will bring it? What do you need to prepare before running the game?

3 Make sure that you all know the instructions and that you agree on the rules. Decide how long the game will run for and who's doing what.

❋ Who'll get the Pack together?

❋ Who's going to explain the game and the rules?

❋ Will someone need to watch for winners?

❋ Should someone keep an eye on the rules being followed?

❋ Do you need to make sure that no one's getting bored?

❋ Who's going to be in charge of safety to make sure no one hurts herself?

4 Sort out with your Guider a good time to do it.

How did it go?

Remember!

Things we need to do.

What we need to get together.

A handy activity

Part of being a Guide is sharing your ideas and skills with the rest of your Patrol. Get in some practise by getting your Six to make or do something together.

Check it out

Have a talk to your Guider about what you'd like to do, then make sure all your Six are happy to give it a go.

Six of the best?

It's really important for Patrols to be good at agreeing what they want to do. Here is one fun way of turning everyone's views into a group decision.

There are lots of goodies to buy from the shop – especially at the sweets counter! Can your Six agree which is the best?

> Check with everyone if there is any sort of sweet they shouldn't eat, then make it a rule not to buy those. **Be safe**

Get an idea

What will everyone have fun doing? Perhaps it could count towards a challenge or a badge?

If you need inspiration look through some books and magazines. Or see if you can find an idea on the television, or from some web sites. Still stuck? Ask your Pack Leader to suggest something!

Web safe

How did it go?

Tried and tested

✿ Try out your idea by yourself so you know exactly what you are doing.

✿ Make a list of everything you will need.

✿ Write the instructions out just in case you get stuck.

✿ Tidy away at the end.

Remember!

Things we need to do.

What we need to get together.

---

1 Ask each person in your Six to bring in a small packet of sweets. Pick ones that have at least six identical small sweets in them.

2 Everyone tries a sweet from each packet then gives it a mark out of 10. A totally yummy sweet gets 10, while 1 means it's yuk!

3 When you've all finished chomping, add up the marks for each sweet. The one with the highest score is your favourite Six sweet!

What do you think?

Do you all like the top sweet even if it's not your number one choice? Now have a go at this activity again. Instead of sweets vote for your favourite game – then play it.

How did it go?

Remember!

Things I need to do.

What I need to get together.

Guide wear

Guides have a great range of clothes to choose from!

One of the things you'll do as a Guide is pick what you want to wear. So you might like to think about the sorts of things you will be doing. After all, it's no good choosing a sweatshirt for a summer dance party!

Ask your Guider for the catalogue showing all the Guide clothes. With your Brownie friends, choose the best outfits for these occasions.

* A Guide meeting in the summer.
* An April Rainbow outing.
* A night hike in September.
* A weekend camp.
* A cooking evening at Guides.
* A Patrol sleepover at someone's house.

Remember, you won't be able to get everything on your list. So before you pick for real, check with your new Guide Patrol what sort of activities they usually get up to.

How did it go?

Guides are friendly

At Guides you'll make lots of new friends. But what is it that makes someone a good friend?

1 Chat with your Brownie friends about what makes a good friend. You might think that a good friend shares, or will always stick up for you, or...

2 Each write on your piece of paper one thing that a good friend means to you.

3 Now agree the most important thing to look for in a good friend. Arrange the pieces of paper into a triangle, so the most important is at the top, the second two on the next row and the other three at the bottom.

You need
A piece of paper and a pencil each.

Write what you agree here.

How did it go?

The hard part is to see if you can all agree on the order!

The G file

To do this challenge you will need to get hold of a G file. Does your Pack Leader have one you can borrow? If not, ask your Guider if she can get one for you.

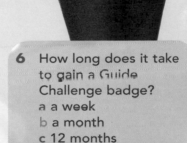

Find the answers to these questions in it.

1 What's the 28th word of the Guide Promise?
a best
b Guide
c country

2 What might you choose to wear for a night hike?
a black trousers
b bright clothing
c t-shirt

3 Who chooses the Patrol Leader?
a Guider
b other Patrol Leaders
c Patrol members

4 Which guiding World Centre is in the UK?
a Pax Lodge
b Our Chalet
c Sangam

5 What is a fun way of helping to make changes to your community?
a community action
b having a barbecue
c going on holiday

6 How long does it take to gain a Guide Challenge badge?
a a week
b a month
c 12 months

7 How old do you need to be to do your Guide Camp Permit?
a 10
b 11½
c 13 or over

8 How many statements are there in the United Nations Convention on the Rights of the Child?
a 10
b more than 50
c almost 200

9 What do you have to do for clause 2 of the Camper badge?
a help pitch and strike a tent
b make a sleeping bag
c know how to find the nearest chip shop

10 When you are an older Guide, what special things can you do?
a parachuting
b go abroad with Guides from around the country
c make candyfloss

How did it go?

89

Guide life!

Play this board game with your Brownie friends.

 Throw again.

 Miss a turn.

Follow the arrow.

You need
one dice ✿ a counter each

You arrive late every week.
12

13

The Pandas have a laugh doing a Go For It! activity.
14

It rains on your Patrol fun day.
26

25

The Pandas raise money for a charity.
24

You join the Panda Patrol.
1

2

11

You gain your Film Lover badge.
15

23

Panda Patrol plan their sleepover!
22

You get your welcome pack.
3

You take eggs for the baking night.
10

16

You sign your unit's Guidelines.
4

You help make a Patrol decision.
9

You forget the football for the 5-a-side match.
17

You flood the meeting place.
21

8

You survive the cook-out night!
20

5

You pick your Guide clothes.
6

You make your Promise at the ice rink.
7

You go to the District music camp.
18

19

 90

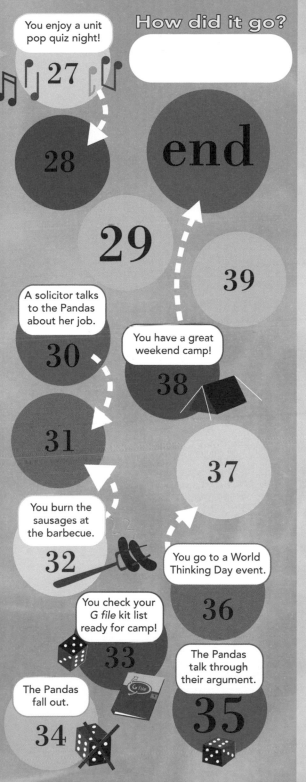

How did it go?

You enjoy a unit pop quiz night!

27

28

end

29

39

A solicitor talks to the Pandas about her job.

30

You have a great weekend camp!

38

31

37

You burn the sausages at the barbecue.

32

You go to a World Thinking Day event.

36

You check your G file kit list ready for camp!

33

The Pandas talk through their argument.

35

The Pandas fall out.

34

Platebag beetle!

When you go to Guide camp there are lots of things you'll need to take with you. Don't worry, because there is a list in the G file.

You'll probably hear the Guides talking about a platebag. This is just what it says – a bag to put your plate, mug, bowl and cutlery in!

This game will help you remember what goes into your platebag.

You need

one die ✿ pen and paper for each person

1 Take turns to throw the die.

2 First, you need to throw a 6. When you get one, draw the outline of your platebag on your paper.

3 Next time it's your turn to throw the die, draw the right item from the list inside your platebag. But remember that you only need one of each item!

1 plate
2 knife
3 bowl
4 fork
5 mug
6 spoon

4 The winner is the one who has all six items in her platebag first.

How did it go?

Celebrate your Adventure

It's almost time to leave Brownies. Hopefully you have had masses of fun on your Brownie Adventure, and your Brownie Promise Box is bursting with things to remind you of your time at Brownies.

So what better way to say goodbye to Brownies and hello to a whole new adventure than having a celebration with all your Brownie friends?

Special to you

As a Brownie you will have done things no one else has done, because you are unique! You will have done some Brownie things like no other Brownie. So make a big deal about them! Make them a cause for your celebration. Think about them here.

My proudest Promise moment.

My best ever challenge.

The best thing about my first Brownie camp or holiday.

The friendliest Brownie I've met from another Pack.

My favourite Six moment.

The badge I was most pleased to get.

The funniest thing that ever happened at Brownies.

My best Adventure Day.

Do it in your style

Are you a bit of a party animal? Or is your idea of fun a burger and cola with a few Brownie friends? However you'd like to celebrate, there's bound to be a special way for you. In case you need some ideas…

* Throw a party with other Brownies who made their Promise at the same time.
* A special activity at Brownie holiday.
* Go with the Brownies on a special outing.
* An exclusive Six party.
* A meeting with a theme of your choice.
* A Brownie meeting where you play all your favourite games.
* A fun night with your Brownie friends.

Ask your Guider, Brownie friends or Six for ideas for your celebration. Fill in here what your ideal celebration would be.

Final plans

Now talk to your Guider about what you'd like to do. Let her help you make your last Brownie adventure really special.

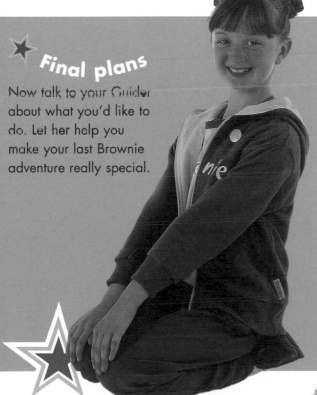

Now get on and do it!
How much fun did you have?

Remember to take lots of photos to keep in your Brownie Promise Box.

Keep in touch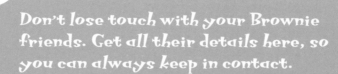

Don't lose touch with your Brownie friends. Get all their details here, so you can always keep in contact.

Name

Six

Address

Postcode

Phone number

Name

Six

Address

Postcode

Phone number

Name

Six

Address

Postcode

Phone number

Name

Six

Address

Postcode

Phone number

Name

Six

Address

Postcode

Phone number

Published by Girlguiding UK, 17–19 Buckingham Palace Road, London, SW1W 0PT
Phone 020 7834 6242 Fax 020 7828 8317 Email chq@girlguiding.org.uk
Web site www.girlguiding.org.uk

Girlguiding UK is an operating name of The Guide Association: incorporated by Royal Charter, registered charity number 306016.

ISBN 0 85260 186 7

Trading Service ordering code 6803

Brownie Renewal Project Manager: Anne Moffat
Senior Project Editor: Alice Forbes
Assistant Project Editor: Elizabeth Duffey
Special Project Designer: David Jones
Designer: Jade Fairman
Studio Team: Sarah Melrose, Heather Peters and Catherine Summers
Illustrators: Martina Farrow and Nila Aye (Go For It! Guides)
Brownie photography: Laura Cartwright
Guide photography (pages 76–89): main photographs Kelvin Rogers, except page 77 Guide in right of group Laura Cartwright: background images Moose Azim, except page 85 Geoff Langam
Additional photography: pages 58–59 Louise Hayley: page 71 (moth) Leonard LeeRue/FLPA: pages 72–73 (Judi Dench) Keith Hayshere: (Evelyn Glennie) James Wilson: (The Queen) The Westmorland Gazette: (Princess Anne) Buckingham Palace Press Office: (Anita Roddick) Vismedia: (JK Rowling) William de la Hay

Printed and bound by Scotprint, Haddington

Used with permission: page 49 (manual alphabet) © RNID: page 69 (fruity chapatis) © World Association of Girl Guides and Girl Scouts, based on a recipe from World Games and Recipes: page 71 (moth) © Leonard LeeRue: page 73 (JK Rowling) © William de la Hay, permission from Bloomsbury Publishing plc.

With thanks to NSPCC for their cooperation in producing the information on pages 34–37.

The Brownie Adventure resulted from the work of the Brownie Development Group: Sandra Moffitt (Brownie Adviser), Helen Channa (Brownie Programme Coordinator), Julia Bennett, Jean Bowers, Gillian Chalmers, Anne Hodder, Emmeline Kirton, Alison Medler, Kirsty Thorburn and Catherine Watson.

Girlguiding UK would like to thank all the Brownies and their Guiders who took part in the consultations and pilot schemes for the development of the Brownie Adventure.

Users are reminded that during the lifespan of this publication there may be changes to
• Girlguiding UK's policy
• legal requirements, practice by governing bodies or British Standards
which will affect the accuracy of the information contained within these pages.

Throughout this book the terms 'parent' and 'daughter' are used. They apply equally to a guardian or other adult with parental responsibility, and their ward.